THE RGO GUIDE

TO THE

1999

TOTAL ECLIPSE

OF THE

SUN

Steve Bell

HM Nautical Almanac Office
Royal Greenwich Observatory
Cambridge

ISBN 0 905 087 03 8

The photograph on the front cover of this guide shows the Sun's outer corona and was taken by Nick Quinn during the total phase of the eclipse of 11th July 1991 as seen from Baja California using a Celestron C90 1000 millimetre $f/11$ telescope.

DISCLAIMER OF LIABILITY

Typeset using TeX

Camera ready copy produced by Cambridge University Press

Printed by The Papworth Press

The RGO Guide to the
1999 Total Eclipse of the Sun

CONTENTS

FOREWORD

On 11 August 1999 there will be a total eclipse of the Sun, visible from parts of Britain; the track will cross Cornwall, Devon and Alderney. This is the first British totality since June 1927, and will be the last for many decades.

Clearly there will be tremendous interest in it, and given clear skies the conditions should be good (though it is true that parts of Europe may be even better). Certainly there is nothing in Nature to rival the glory of totality, but one needs to know just what to expect, and it is also important to remember that direct telescopic or binocular observation of the Sun, except during the actual time of totality, is fraught with danger.

This booklet will explain what will be seen, and provides guidance for those who have no prior experience of eclipses. Let us hope for clear skies on 11 August 1999!

Patrick Moore

ACKNOWLEDGMENTS

I would like to thank my colleagues in HM Nautical Almanac Office both past and present, namely David Harper, Catherine Hohenkerk, Andrew Sinclair, Don Taylor and Bernard Yallop for their assistance in the production of this eclipse guide. In particular, I would like to thank Julie Loaker for her help in preparing the colour plates and the cover of the eclipse guide.

I would also like to express my gratitude to the staff of the Royal Greenwich Observatory for their comments on the drafts of the eclipse guide. My thanks also go to Nick Quinn and Michael Maunder for supplying their excellent eclipse photographs and to all those who have made suggestions leading to the improvement of the content of this version of the eclipse guide. Weather information has been provided in part by the National Meteorological Library and Archive.

Steve Bell
HM Nautical Almanac Office
1997 October

THE 1999 TOTAL ECLIPSE OF THE SUN

1 — Introduction

On the morning of Wednesday 11th August 1999, a total eclipse of the Sun will be visible from the south-western part of the UK mainland, the Isles of Scilly and the Channel Islands, lasting up to 2m 06s. The path of totality starts at sunrise to the south of Nova Scotia and passes over the Atlantic Ocean towards the UK. It then crosses the English Channel, the Cherbourg peninsula, northern France, the southern tip of Belgium and Luxembourg and moves on to southern Germany. After passing over Austria, Hungary and the north-eastern tip of Yugoslavia, the eclipse reaches its maximum duration of totality over Romania before crossing the north-eastern part of Bulgaria and the Black Sea. It then passes over central Turkey, the north-eastern tip of Syria, north-eastern Iraq, Iran, southern Pakistan, central India and ends at sunset over the Bay of Bengal. A partial eclipse will be seen by the north-eastern part of North America, Greenland, Iceland, the rest of the United Kingdom, the Irish Republic, the remainder of Europe, the northern half of Africa, the Middle East and much of Asia as far east as Thailand and central China.

This guide has been produced with the aim of helping people to get the most out of this spectacular event. Although the eclipse has the potential of being seen by the largest number of people in the history of eclipse watching, this guide concentrates on the event as it will be seen from the British Isles. An additional section has been included on the visibility of the eclipse for those people travelling in Europe. Assuming the weather conditions are good, this will be the only opportunity to see a total eclipse of the Sun for nearly one hundred years from the British Isles.

2 — What is an eclipse?

As the Moon orbits the Earth it is said to be in opposition when the Sun and Moon are diametrically opposite each other in the sky. This occurs when the Moon is full. When the Sun and Moon lie in the same direction they are said to be in conjunction and the Moon is new. In the course of a year, there are occasions when the Sun, Earth and Moon are in alignment. When this happens one body will cast a shadow on the other causing an eclipse. If the orbits of the Earth and the Moon were in the same plane, lunar eclipses would occur every full Moon and solar eclipses every new Moon. As the orbital plane of the Moon is inclined at 5° to that of the Earth, the frequency with which these alignments take place is much reduced. For an eclipse to occur the Moon has to be close to one of two points where the orbital planes of the Earth and Moon intersect, in addition to being either new or full. If the new Moon is at either of these intersections, a solar eclipse will take place. If the Moon is full, a lunar eclipse will occur.

The Sun is 400 times the diameter of the Moon but it is also 400 times further away from the Earth. This fortuitous coincidence means that on average the two objects appear to have similar angular sizes in the sky, a unique occurrence in the Solar System. If the orbits of the Earth and Moon were circular, solar eclipses would always be total as the relative distances between the Earth and the Sun and the Earth and the Moon would be constant. In reality, the orbits of the Earth and Moon are ellipses, or elongated circles. As a result, the apparent angular diameter of the Sun varies by about 2% and that of the Moon varies by about 8%. If an alignment takes place when the Moon is further away than its average distance of 384 000 kilometres from the Earth, its apparent diameter is not sufficient to obscure the Sun completely. This causes the central portion of the Sun to be eclipsed leaving a bright ring of sunlight around the Moon. This type of eclipse is known as an annular eclipse.

If the alignment occurs when the Moon is nearer the Earth than its average distance, a total eclipse takes place. This configuration is shown in Figure 1. The Sun is not a point source of light and produces umbral and penumbral shadows when eclipsed by the Moon. In an umbral shadow, none of the light from the Sun can be observed from a point within the shadow. A penumbral shadow is formed when light from the Sun is not completely cut off by the Moon. If the umbral shadow reaches the Earth then a very small portion of the Earth's surface will see a total eclipse. As all the bodies are in motion, the umbral shadow travels rapidly across the face of the Earth from west to east. The movement of the shadow is known as the path of totality. Those areas in the penumbral shadow will see a partial eclipse.

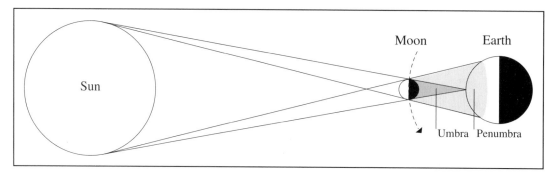

Figure 1: The configuration of the Sun, Moon and Earth during a total eclipse of the Sun. This is a schematic diagram looking down on the north pole of the Earth and is not drawn to scale. The umbral shadow is the darker grey area between the Moon and the Earth and the penumbral shadow is the light grey area. A total eclipse will be seen within the umbral shadow whereas a partial eclipse will be seen within the penumbral shadow.

In the case of an annular eclipse, the umbral shadow just fails to reach the surface of the Earth which lies directly behind the end of the Moon's umbral shadow in a region known as the antumbra. If the alignment of the Sun, Moon and Earth is not sufficiently precise and the Earth intercepts the Moon's penumbral shadow but not the umbral one, then a partial eclipse will be seen by some fraction of the Earth's surface. Occasionally, the umbral shadow of the Moon may only reach the Earth when the Moon is close to its conjunction with the Sun. In these circumstances, we see an eclipse that starts as an annular one, becomes total and then reverts to being annular once more. This "hybrid" eclipse is known as an annular-total eclipse and occurs relatively rarely.

In the case of lunar eclipses, any observer on the Earth can see an eclipse of the Moon as long as the Moon is above the horizon. The shadow cast by the Earth is much larger than the Moon itself and we can observe either penumbral or umbral lunar eclipses. Of these two types of eclipse, penumbral eclipses of the Moon are generally more difficult to detect as the resulting dimming of light tends to be quite small. The majority of observed lunar eclipses, both partial and total, tend to be umbral eclipses. Many people will have seen the coppery-red appearance of the Moon during a total lunar eclipse caused by light reaching the Moon that has been refracted through the Earth's atmosphere. Lunar eclipses are usually much longer than solar eclipses. At most, a total eclipse of the Sun can be as long as $7^m\ 31^s$ and an annular eclipse can last $12^m\ 30^s$, but a total lunar eclipse can last 100 minutes or more.

3 — Predicting eclipses

How can eclipses be predicted? The general circumstances required for a solar eclipse to take place are described in Section 2. The new Moon must lie near the points of intersection between its orbital plane and that of the Earth. These points are known as the nodes and are important in characterizing the orientation of the orbit. These nodes are not stationary but move in the opposite direction to the motion of the Moon at a little over $0°05$ per day. Consequently, the Moon takes 27·21 days to move from one node back to the same node again. This interval is known as a Draconic month. For the Moon to pass from one new Moon to the next takes 29·53 days, an interval known as a lunation. If the new Moon was at one of its nodes, it would take 242 Draconic months or 223 lunations to get back to the same configuration. In this interval of a little over 18 years and 10 days, the Sun returns to the same node of the Moon's orbit nineteen times. Consequently, if an eclipse occurred at the beginning of this cycle, another eclipse would occur some 18 years and 10 days later. This cycle, known as the Saros cycle, was known to the Babylonians more than 2500 years ago from their observations of lunar eclipses.

The Babylonians also noticed that the eclipses that occurred at the Saros interval were of similar types. For one annular eclipse to follow another on an 18 year time scale, the Moon must be further away than its average distance from the Earth on both occasions. Similarly for two total eclipses to follow each other, the Moon must be closer than its average distance from the Earth on both occasions. Hence, another cycle must play a part in the Saros cycle. We know that for the Moon to go once round its elliptical orbit takes 27·55 days, a period known as an anomalistic month. During the Saros cycle, the Moon completes 239 orbits and therefore returns to a similar position in its orbit and hence a similar distance from the Earth in a little over 18 years. Consequently, all these cycles mesh together to permit the recurrence of similar types of eclipses at 18 year intervals.

A Saros series is made up of many individual Saros cycles. Each Saros series is composed of between 69 and 86 eclipses and lasts on average 1400 years. At any one time 42 Saros series are running simultaneously. The Saros series starts with partial eclipses in the polar regions of the Earth, builds up to annular or total eclipses in the equatorial regions and ends in partial eclipses at the opposite pole. The Saros cycle is not perfect because the underlying lunar cycles are not totally synchronized. Consequently, consecutive eclipses in a Saros series do not occur at the same geographical location, they are shifted westwards by about 120° in longitude. The match between eclipse circumstances is better over three Saros cycles, although the eclipse tracks are now shifted either north or south. This 54 year interval is called the Triple Saros.

Modern techniques for calculating eclipses use high precision numerical computations such as those produced by NASA's Jet Propulsion Laboratory to determine the positions of the Earth and Moon relative to the Sun. These precise positions with respect to time are known as ephemerides. Using techniques developed by F.W. Bessel, a nineteenth century German mathematician, it is possible to characterize the geometric position of the shadow of the Moon relative to the Earth. Eclipse maps can then be generated from these calculations such as those reproduced in *The Astronomical Almanac*. These maps show the central path if any, the region of visibility of the eclipse and the timings of specific phases of the eclipse. The appearance of an eclipse from a specific location or "local circumstances" can also be determined.

Coordinated Universal Time (UTC) is the basis of civil time-keeping and it is adjusted to conform closely to the daily motion of the stars due to the rotation of the Earth. However, this rotation is subject to small unpredictable variations. The ephemerides that are used to predict eclipses, however, are based on a uniform time scale called dynamical time. A correction ΔT, (pronounced delta tee), has to be applied to dynamical time to obtain UTC. In this guide we are adopting a value of $\Delta T = 65\cdot5$ seconds for the total eclipse of 11th August 1999. In the context of this guide, Greenwich Mean Time (GMT) is synonymous with UTC. However, during the summer months in the British Isles, Summer Time (BST) is in force, which is one hour ahead of GMT. As the eclipse takes place during August, **all times quoted in this guide are given in BST**.

What conditions are necessary for a good solar eclipse? The best opportunity to get a total eclipse of the Sun is when the Moon is closest to the Earth and its angular size is greatest. The apparent diameter of the Sun should also be as small as possible. This occurs when the distance from the Earth to the Sun is greatest, a point in the Earth's orbit called aphelion which occurs in early July. To prolong the eclipse as much as possible, it should take place in the equatorial regions of the Earth where the surface velocity reaches a maximum value of 1700 kilometres per hour and cancels out some of the motion of the shadow of the Moon which moves at approximately 3400 kilometres per hour. The Moon is also slightly closer to us when it is at the zenith or directly overhead. This can extend totality by a few seconds. At best, the width of the Moon's umbral shadow can reach 269 kilometres and the duration of totality can reach $7^m 31^s$. In the case of an annular eclipse, the antumbral shadow can be as wide as 313 kilometres with eclipses lasting up to $12^m 30^s$. The path of the eclipse can be much wider than these limits due to the projection of the shadow on the Earth's surface.

4 — The Sun

The Sun is a normal star and is special only in that it is so close to us. This makes it easier to study than other stars because the closest of them is some 250 000 times further away. A total eclipse of the Sun gives observers on the Earth an opportunity to study the extended atmosphere of the Sun which is invisible under normal circumstances. In order to understand some of the phenomena we see at an eclipse, a brief description of the structure of the Sun is needed.

The Sun's energy is generated by nuclear reactions fuelled by hydrogen in a very dense core about the size of Jupiter where the temperature reaches 15 000 000° C. The core is surrounded by a mixture of hydrogen and helium and a small proportion of heavier elements with a composition identical to that from which the Sun was originally made. The flow of energy from the core passes through progressively less dense layers of the Sun until it reaches a region called the convective zone where the flow becomes turbulent. This region is the source of the solar magnetic field. Above this layer is the visible face of the Sun called the photosphere. It is only 500 kilometres thick (0·1% of the solar radius) and is the home of such familiar features as sunspots. We cannot see further into the Sun than this layer as it is completely opaque. In the central regions of the solar disk, we can see deeper into the hotter, denser regions of the Sun's photosphere than we can near the edge or limb of the Sun. Therefore the Sun appears brighter in the centre than it does at the limb. Light from the photosphere must then pass through the chromosphere or "colour-sphere" and the corona to reach us.

On average, the chromosphere is about 4000 kilometres thick. The name is derived from its pinkish colour caused by an atomic transition of hydrogen. Beyond this layer is the corona which extends millions of kilometres into space. It is a region of plasma whose temperature is 1 000 000° C and whose density is so low that one gramme of material occupies more than one cubic kilometre. Both the chromosphere and the corona can only be observed by the naked eye during total eclipses unless special equipment is used. Disturbances in the chromosphere called spicules can reach 15 000 kilometres into the corona but these substantial features are overshadowed by the more spectacular prominences. These arches of glowing gas can reach 250 000 kilometres into the corona and can sometimes be seen during totality. When activity on the Sun is at the peak of its 11 year cycle, as it was in 1991, the corona is seen as a complex structure exhibiting many streamers which can extend many solar radii into space. Early observations of the shape of the corona pointed to the existence of magnetic fields in the Sun long before they were actually measured. The pattern of the streamers in the corona bear a strong resemblance to the configuration that iron filings adopt in the presence of a bar magnet. At the minimum of the solar cycle, much of the activity is confined to the solar equator.

5 — The last total eclipse visible in the British Isles

With the exception of the total eclipse of 30th June 1954 which was visible only in the northernmost part of the Shetland Islands, the last total eclipse of the Sun visible in the United Kingdom mainland took place seventy years ago. On 29th June 1927, not long after sunrise, the path of totality in the UK crossed the coast of Cardigan Bay to the west of Porthmadog, passed to the east of Colwyn Bay and out over the Irish Sea. It crossed the coastline again at Southport and moved north east over Settle, Richmond, Darlington and West Hartlepool and then out over the North Sea. Totality lasted a little less than 25 seconds and was seen from a strip of land 50 kilometres wide. For the rest of the UK, the eclipse was seen as a partial one.

6 — The August 1999 total eclipse

Fortunately, the total eclipse of 11th August 1999 takes place during late morning when the Sun will be relatively high in the sky. It will be visible from the Isles of Scilly, most of Cornwall, western Devon and Alderney in the Channel Islands. The total eclipse will be seen from a strip of land a little over 100 kilometres wide and totality will last a maximum of 2m 06s in the British Isles.

In a global context, the path of totality starts at sunrise approximately 400 kilometres south of Halifax, Nova Scotia and crosses the Atlantic Ocean where its first landfall is the Cornish peninsula close to Land's End. After passing over south-west England and Alderney in the Channel Islands, it crosses the Cherbourg peninsula, passing over northern France, the southern tip of Belgium, and Luxembourg, southern Germany, Austria, Hungary, the north-eastern tip of Yugoslavia, Romania, the north-eastern part of Bulgaria and out over the Black Sea. The path of totality then crosses over central Turkey, the north eastern tip of Syria, north-eastern Iraq, Iran, southern Pakistan, central India and ends at sunset over the Bay of Bengal approximately 500 kilometres east of the Indian city of Srikakulam. The maximum duration of totality takes place over Romania at $11^h 59^m$ BST reaching $2^m 27^s$. The paths of the umbral and penumbral shadows are shown in Figure 2. A partial eclipse of the Sun will be seen in the north-eastern part of North America, Greenland, Iceland, Europe, North Africa, the Middle East and much of Asia as far east as Thailand and central China.

Figure 2: The path of the umbral and penumbral shadows of the total eclipse of 11th August 1999. The area shaded in dark grey is the path of totality of the eclipse whereas the lighter shading indicates those areas where a partial eclipse will be visible. The dark vertical bars running across the path of totality are spaced at 15 minute intervals. The bar to the south west of Ireland represents the point of maximum eclipse at $11^h 00^m$ BST.

In a historical context, this eclipse is the 21st in a total of 77 eclipses in Saros series 145. Lasting just under 1400 years, this Saros series consists of 34 partial eclipses, 41 total eclipses, one annular and one annular/total eclipse. The series began on 4th January 1639 as a marginal partial eclipse in the North Polar regions. It will end on 17th April 3009 in a similar fashion in the South Polar regions. As Saros series 145 matures, the duration of totality for each eclipse will gradually increase to more than seven minutes for the eclipse of 25th June 2522 as the eclipse tracks themselves move towards the equator.

7 — What do you see during a total eclipse of the Sun?

The beginning of a solar eclipse is known as "first contact". This is the moment when the Moon begins to obscure the Sun's photosphere, giving the appearance of a "bite" taken from the edge of the very bright solar disk. The "partial phase" follows where progressively more and more of the Sun's photosphere is obscured by the Moon. Shortly before totality, the Moon's shadow can be seen approaching from the western horizon, giving the impression of an approaching storm and the sky darkens noticeably. This partial phase lasts about an hour or so until "second contact" when the Sun is hidden by the Moon, leaving the last remnants of the Sun's photosphere as a thin silvery ring around the limb of the Moon.

During the partial phases of the eclipse, you may see many hundreds of images of the crescent Sun on the ground beneath trees. This phenomenon is caused by the gaps in the foliage acting as pinhole cameras focusing the crescent image of the Sun. In the few minutes before second contact, the sky darkens noticeably and both flora and fauna react to the increasing darkness. Some flowers may close up, animals may behave as they would at nightfall and birds may go to roost. As the amount of light diminishes more rapidly, the landscape can take on a metallic grey hue and shadows become sharper. The temperature may also drop by a couple of degrees. An elusive phenomenon known as "shadow bands" may also be observed which give the appearance of parallel light and dark bands moving rapidly across the ground. These ripples are caused by irregular atmospheric refraction of the crescent shaped image of the Sun and may appear again in the few minutes after the end of totality.

Just before totality, the bright photospheric ring around the Sun breaks up into discrete blobs of light known as Baily's Beads. This effect is caused by the final flashes of sunlight shining through some of the gaps between the lunar mountain ranges on the eastern limb of the Moon. Within a few seconds all the "beads" disappear except one. Nearly all of the bright photosphere is gone and the Sun's corona becomes visible as a pearly white ring, sometimes irregular in shape, around the Sun. The final bright spot of the photosphere in conjunction with the ring formed by the inner corona give rise to the so-called "diamond ring effect". Within seconds this feature disappears and the corona comes into full view. Totality has now begun.

During totality, the entire horizon may appear orange or maroon resembling the colours of the sky after sunset. The colour of the sky in the direction from which the shadow of the Moon is approaching is usually a purple colour. Bright stars and planets can be seen during totality. The Sun's corona can now be seen clearly, extending radially away from the Sun in all directions. It is pearly white in colour and may extend several solar radii from the Sun depending on how active the Sun is at the time of the eclipse. At the minimum of solar activity, the Sun's magnetic field binds the coronal gas into streamers. These streamers are wide at their base close to the Sun's limb and curl up to a point. At the poles of the Sun, the streamers take on the appearance of thin streams of gas, like iron filings following the magnetic field of a bar magnet. The more active the Sun, the greater the number of streamers from a wider range of latitudes. When the Sun is at its most active, the corona may appear as a broad ring-like feature. As the Sun is expected to be close to maximum activity in 1999, we can look forward to an active corona during this particular eclipse. You may be able to see the chromosphere of the Sun as a pinkish ring around the edge of the Moon's disk. Sometimes, when the Sun is particularly active you might be able to see signs of prominences, pinkish arcs of gas within the inner regions of the corona and the chromosphere.

At "third contact", the total phase of the eclipse is over. What was seen in the moments before totality now occurs in reverse time order. A second "diamond ring" may appear followed by another display of Baily's Beads on the western limb of the Moon. The Moon's shadow can be seen heading towards the eastern horizon shortly after the end of totality. The Sun's photosphere brightens rapidly after totality and the eclipse finishes when the silhouette of the

Moon disappears at "fourth contact". Examples of what you might see during the different stages of the eclipse are shown in Plates 1 – 4.

Figure 3 shows the configuration of the Sun and Moon at different times during the eclipse and also the points on the Moon's limb where Baily's Beads may occur. The first panel shows the relative positions of the Sun and Moon at first contact. The Moon is shown as a black disk in Figure 3 simply to illustrate its position. In reality, we can only detect its position by the way it obscures the Sun's disk. Forty minutes after first contact, the Sun will appear as a crescent shape as shown in the second panel.

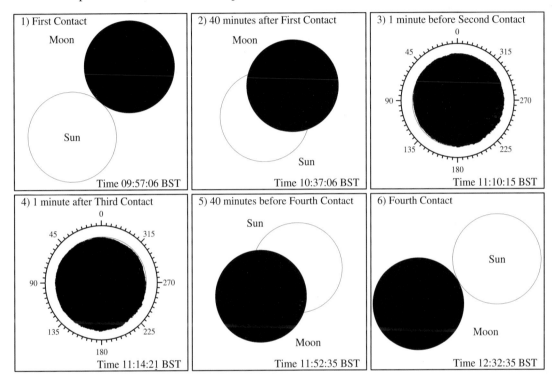

Figure 3: The configuration of the Sun and Moon at different times during the eclipse as viewed from Falmouth. The features on the lunar limb have been exaggerated for the panels just before second contact and just after third contact for the reasons outlined in Section 7. This also illustrates how features on the lunar limb give rise to Baily's Beads just before second contact and just after third contact. The third and fourth panels also show how position angle (PA) is defined in this guide. Further information on position angles can be found in Section 9.

The third panel shows the eclipse configuration one minute before second contact. The features on the lunar limb have been exaggerated to show the lunar valleys and mountains more clearly. The profile of the Moon used here is based on measurements by C.R. Watts derived from a photographic atlas of the Moon. Baily's Beads may be visible where a gap exists between the solid outline of the Moon and the photospheric disk of the Sun. At second contact, the Moon completely obscures the Sun and the total phase of the eclipse has begun. The Sun remains obscured until third contact. These two phases have been omitted from Figure 3. The fourth panel shows the configuration one minute after third contact when the Sun's disk reappears. The features on the limb have been enhanced in the same way as those in the third panel. The last two panels show the relative positions of the Sun and Moon forty minutes before fourth contact and at fourth contact. Although this diagram shows the local circumstances for Falmouth, the overall appearance of the eclipse should be similar at any point on the path of totality over the UK and the Channel Islands although the times will be different. Local circumstances for the British Isles will be discussed more fully in Sections 9 and 10.

For those people who can observe the total eclipse but are located close to the edge of the path of totality, there is some compensation for the brevity of the total phase of the eclipse.

The duration of the display of Baily's Beads increases as you move closer to the edge of the path of totality. The southern edge of the path will provide a better display of beads because the lunar landscape is more rugged near the Moon's south pole.

8 — Using the guide

The next two sections of this guide describe how the eclipse will be seen from different parts of the UK, the Irish Republic and the Channel Islands. The timing and appearance of an eclipse from a particular place are known as "local circumstances". These circumstances will be different for every location. As the path of the eclipse moves eastwards at supersonic speeds so observers in Cork will see maximum eclipse more than 13 minutes before those in Norwich. The majority of observers in the British Isles will see a partial eclipse and Section 9 includes a discussion of the eclipse as they will see it. Those observers lucky enough to be in the path of totality can find a description of their view of the eclipse in Section 10.

The two most important pieces of information about the eclipse are shown in Figure 4. The lines drawn almost vertically join together points having the same times of maximum eclipse, the moment when the area of the Sun's disk obscured by the Moon is greatest. The nearly horizontal lines join together places seeing the same degree of obscuration at maximum eclipse. Symbols showing the relative positions of the Sun and Moon at maximum eclipse for the relevant degrees of obscuration are given at the right hand side of the map. In the lower half of the diagram, the northern and southern limits of the path of totality have been plotted as well as the central line of the eclipse. A more detailed map of the path of totality showing the Isles of Scilly, south-west England, the Channel Islands and northern France is given in Figure 5.

To illustrate the purpose of Figure 4, let us use a simple example. It can be seen that Lincoln, Aberdeen and Kirkwall will all experience the greatest obscuration of the Sun at approximately $11^h 20^m$ BST. However, Lincoln will see an obscuration of 90·7%, Aberdeen will see 77·6% and Kirkwall will see only 71·9% of the Sun disappear. To put these figures into perspective, an obscuration of 85% will cause the ambient light level to drop noticeably. Consequently, Wales, Northern Ireland, the Irish Republic and most of England will see a measurable darkening of the sky at maximum eclipse. However, in northern England and Scotland, the effect will be less noticeable.

9 — Local circumstances of the partial eclipse in the British Isles

Table 1 gives local circumstances for 110 cities and towns across the UK and the Irish Republic. These locations have been selected to provide a reasonable geographical distribution over the two countries. As the eclipse will be seen as a partial one from all of these places, times of first and fourth contact have been given. Times of second and third contact are only applicable to those locations seeing totality. In order to explain the meaning of the information given in Table 1, let us use Cambridge as an example.

The first column in the table refers to the location and the next four columns refer to first contact. The time of first contact or the beginning of the eclipse is $10^h 04^m 32^s$ BST. The position of the Sun in the sky is described by its azimuth and altitude. Azimuth (Az) is measured clockwise from true north through east, south, west and back to north. It should be noted that magnetic north is not the same as true north. *Polaris*, the Pole Star, lies within 1° of true north whereas magnetic north will lie some 5° west of true north for most parts of the UK by 1999. True north corresponds to an azimuth of 0°, east to 90°, south to 180° and west to 270°.

At the start of the eclipse in Cambridge, the Sun lies at an azimuth of 119° which corresponds to approximately east south east. The Sun is at an altitude (Alt) of 39°, that is to say that it is 39° above the horizon. The sea-level horizon has an altitude of 0° and the point in the sky directly overhead has an altitude of 90°. The silhouette of the Moon first appears on the Sun's disk at a position angle (PA) of 313°. In order to understand the term position angle, let us make an analogy between position angle and the direction of the hour hand on a clock face at different times.

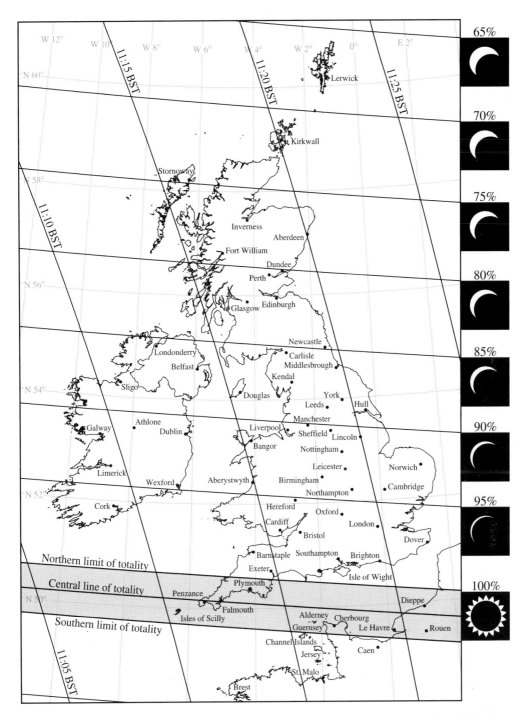

Figure 4: The circumstances of the eclipse for the UK mainland and the Irish Republic. The near vertical lines link sites having the same times of maximum eclipse whereas those running nearly horizontally link places experiencing the same degree of obscuration at maximum eclipse. Times of maximum eclipse are given in British Summer Time (BST) at five minute intervals. The appearance of the Sun at maximum eclipse is shown for the relevant obscuration on the right hand side of the diagram. The diagram for 100% obscuration simulates the appearance of the corona and streamers. The latitude and longitude lines and annotation are shown in grey. The shaded area is the path of totality. The northern and southern limits of the path of totality are indicated as well as the central line of the eclipse.

Table 1: Local circumstances of the partial eclipse in the British Isles

Place	First Contact				Maximum Eclipse					Fourth Contact			
	Time	Az	Alt	PA	Time	Az	Alt	Mag	Obs	Time	Az	Alt	PA
	h m s	°	°	°	h m s	°	°			h m s	°	°	°
Aberdeen	10 08 26	121	36	300	11 20 02	141	43	0·818	0·776	12 34 39	166	48	123
Aberystwyth	10 00 32	114	36	314	11 14 56	134	45	0·949	0·942	12 33 36	161	52	120
Athlone	09 58 20	110	33	312	11 10 47	129	42	0·924	0·912	11 27 46	154	50	125
Ayr	10 03 52	116	35	306	11 16 06	136	43	0·866	0·837	12 32 00	161	49	124
Bangor, Gwynedd	10 01 26	114	36	312	11 15 20	135	45	0·927	0·914	12 33 20	161	51	121
Barnstaple	09 59 04	113	36	317	11 14 12	133	46	0·986	0·987	12 33 54	161	53	119
Barrow-in-Furness	10 03 22	116	36	309	11 16 58	137	45	0·901	0·881	12 34 21	163	50	121
Bath	10 01 05	115	37	316	11 16 41	136	47	0·975	0·975	12 36 30	165	53	117
Belfast	10 01 35	114	34	308	11 14 01	133	43	0·891	0·869	12 30 29	158	49	124
Berwick-on-Tweed	10 06 37	120	36	304	11 19 22	140	44	0·855	0·823	12 35 23	166	49	122
Bideford	09 58 52	112	36	318	11 13 58	133	46	0·988	0·990	12 33 41	160	53	119
Birmingham	10 02 50	117	37	313	11 17 57	138	46	0·943	0·935	12 36 57	166	52	118
Blackburn	10 03 38	117	37	310	11 17 43	138	45	0·910	0·893	12 35 33	165	51	120
Blackpool	10 03 12	116	36	310	11 17 03	137	45	0·908	0·891	12 34 42	164	51	121
Bournemouth	10 00 53	115	38	318	11 17 01	136	48	0·993	0·995	12 37 26	165	54	116
Bradford	10 04 24	118	37	309	11 18 41	139	46	0·907	0·890	12 36 35	166	51	119
Brighton	10 02 52	117	39	317	11 19 33	139	49	0·986	0·988	12 40 11	169	54	114
Bristol	10 00 56	115	37	316	11 16 25	136	47	0·974	0·973	12 36 09	164	53	117
Bude	09 58 20	112	36	318	11 13 24	132	46	0·993	0·995	12 33 10	160	53	119
Cambridge	10 04 32	119	39	313	11 20 28	141	48	0·948	0·941	12 40 02	170	53	115
Canterbury	10 04 41	119	40	315	11 21 31	142	49	0·971	0·970	12 41 58	172	54	113
Cardiff	10 00 21	114	37	316	11 15 35	135	46	0·973	0·972	12 35 08	163	53	118
Carlisle	10 04 39	118	36	307	11 17 48	138	44	0·879	0·854	12 34 31	164	50	122
Carmarthen	09 59 40	113	36	315	11 14 18	133	45	0·965	0·962	12 33 22	160	52	120
Chester	10 02 35	116	36	311	11 16 54	137	45	0·926	0·913	12 35 08	164	51	120
Cork	09 56 01	108	33	316	11 09 04	127	43	0·966	0·964	12 27 04	152	51	124
Coventry	10 03 05	117	38	313	11 18 21	138	47	0·945	0·937	12 37 29	167	52	117
Cowes	10 01 34	116	38	317	11 17 54	137	48	0·991	0·993	12 38 23	167	54	115
Crediton	09 59 10	113	37	318	11 14 37	133	47	0·994	0·995	12 34 37	162	53	118
Derby	10 03 38	117	37	312	11 18 35	139	46	0·931	0·920	12 37 18	167	52	118
Devizes	10 01 28	115	38	316	11 17 12	137	47	0·975	0·975	12 37 06	165	53	117
Doncaster	10 04 43	119	38	310	11 19 22	140	46	0·914	0·898	12 37 36	168	51	118
Douglas	10 02 16	115	35	309	11 15 27	135	44	0·902	0·882	12 32 35	161	50	122
Dover	10 04 48	119	40	315	11 21 49	142	49	0·975	0·975	12 42 25	173	54	113
Dublin	09 59 41	112	34	312	11 12 47	131	43	0·925	0·912	12 30 14	157	50	123
Dumfries	10 04 14	117	35	306	11 17 03	137	44	0·876	0·849	12 33 30	163	49	122
Dundee	10 06 39	119	35	302	11 18 35	139	43	0·838	0·801	12 33 47	164	48	123
Durham	10 05 46	119	37	306	11 19 24	140	45	0·881	0·855	12 36 25	167	50	120
Eastbourne	10 03 18	118	39	317	11 20 11	140	49	0·987	0·989	12 40 56	170	54	113
Edinburgh	10 05 45	118	35	304	11 18 02	138	43	0·852	0·819	12 33 42	164	48	123
Exeter	09 59 14	113	37	318	11 14 46	133	47	0·995	0·997	12 34 50	162	53	118
Exmouth	09 59 15	113	37	319	11 14 53	134	47	0·998	0·999	12 35 03	162	54	117
Fort William	10 05 20	117	34	302	11 16 25	136	42	0·831	0·792	12 30 57	160	47	125
Galway	09 57 16	109	32	313	11 09 25	127	42	0·928	0·916	12 26 14	152	49	126
Glasgow	10 04 45	117	35	304	11 16 48	137	43	0·855	0·823	12 32 22	162	48	124
Gloucester	10 01 45	116	37	315	11 17 06	137	47	0·961	0·957	12 36 33	165	53	117
Great Yarmouth	10 06 43	121	40	311	11 22 52	144	48	0·933	0·922	12 42 16	174	53	114
Hereford	10 01 28	115	37	314	11 16 33	136	46	0·957	0·952	12 35 46	164	52	118
Hexham	10 05 30	119	36	306	11 18 50	139	45	0·876	0·850	12 35 36	166	50	121
Hull	10 05 45	120	38	309	11 20 30	141	46	0·906	0·888	12 38 38	169	51	118
Ilfracombe	09 59 09	113	36	317	11 14 11	133	46	0·982	0·983	12 33 46	161	53	119
Inverness	10 06 57	118	34	300	11 17 47	138	42	0·814	0·770	12 31 49	162	47	125
Ipswich	10 05 32	120	40	313	11 21 54	143	48	0·949	0·943	12 41 42	172	53	114
Kendal	10 04 05	117	36	308	11 17 41	138	45	0·894	0·873	12 34 57	164	50	121
Kirkwall	10 10 16	122	35	296	11 20 06	141	41	0·773	0·719	12 32 42	165	46	126

Times are given in British Summer Time (BST = GMT + 1ʰ)

Plate 1: If there are trees near the location from which you are observing the total eclipse of 11th August 1999, many images of the crescent Sun may be visible in the shadows beneath those trees during the partial phase of the eclipse. This phenomenon is caused by gaps in the foliage acting as pinhole cameras which focus the image of the Sun. In this 10th May 1994 photograph of an annular eclipse taken in Arizona, many images of the eclipsed Sun can be seen.

© *Michael Maunder*

Plate 2: Photographs of solar eclipses need not simply feature the Sun. Capturing the effect that the total eclipse has on your surroundings can be just as rewarding. In this wide-angle photograph of the total eclipse of the Sun taken on the morning of 23rd October 1976 from Zanzibar, the eclipsed Sun can be seen against the inverted cone-shaped shadow of the Moon.

© *Michael Maunder*

Plate 3: One of the most beautiful sights to be seen during a total eclipse of the Sun is the so-called 'diamond ring effect'. This feature is caused by the last rays of sunlight passing between features on the lunar limb. This photograph was taken using a Celestron C90 1000 millimetre f/11 telescope at the moment of third contact during the eclipse of 3rd November 1994 in Chile. Prominences can also be seen as red dots in the pearly white inner corona of the Sun.

© *Nick Quinn*

Plate 4: Without special equipment, the Sun's corona can only be seen during a total eclipse of the Sun. This photograph was taken during the total phase of the eclipse of 3rd November 1994 as seen from Chile using a Celestron C90 1000 millimetre f/11 telescope. The corona can be seen as a broad feature surrounding the Sun exhibiting considerable structure. Equatorial streamers and polar brushes can also be seen.

© *Nick Quinn*

Table 1: Local circumstances of the partial eclipse in the British Isles (continued)

Place	First Contact				Maximum Eclipse					Fourth Contact			
	Time	Az	Alt	PA	Time	Az	Alt	Mag	Obs	Time	Az	Alt	PA
	h m s	°	°	°	h m s	°	°			h m s	°	°	°
Lancaster	10 03 42	117	36	309	11 17 29	138	45	0·902	0·883	12 34 59	164	50	121
Launceston	09 58 19	112	36	319	11 13 33	132	46	0·999	0·999	12 33 30	160	53	119
Leeds	10 04 36	118	37	309	11 18 55	139	46	0·906	0·888	12 36 48	167	51	119
Leicester	10 03 44	118	38	312	11 19 01	139	47	0·938	0·929	12 38 02	168	52	117
Lerwick	10 13 30	125	35	292	11 22 38	145	41	0·741	0·679	12 34 07	168	45	126
Limerick	09 56 50	109	33	314	11 09 26	127	42	0·945	0·937	12 26 50	152	50	125
Lincoln	10 04 57	119	38	310	11 19 59	141	47	0·921	0·907	12 38 34	169	52	117
Liverpool	10 02 49	116	36	311	11 16 59	137	45	0·920	0·905	12 35 02	164	51	120
Llandrindod Wells	10 01 01	114	36	314	11 15 45	135	46	0·952	0·947	12 34 42	163	52	119
London (Central)	10 03 31	118	39	315	11 19 49	140	48	0·968	0·966	12 39 54	169	53	115
Londonderry	10 00 57	112	33	308	11 12 40	131	42	0·881	0·856	12 28 29	156	48	126
Lundy Island	09 58 35	112	36	317	11 13 27	132	46	0·984	0·985	12 32 56	159	53	119
Luton	10 03 38	118	39	314	11 19 37	140	48	0·958	0·953	12 39 21	169	53	115
Manchester	10 03 34	117	37	310	11 17 53	138	46	0·916	0·901	12 35 58	165	51	119
Margate	10 05 09	120	40	314	11 22 01	143	49	0·967	0·965	12 42 24	173	54	113
Merthyr Tydfil	10 00 29	114	37	315	11 15 30	135	46	0·966	0·963	12 34 49	162	53	119
Middlesborough	10 05 51	119	37	307	11 19 43	141	45	0·885	0·862	12 36 58	167	50	120
Minehead	09 59 47	113	37	317	11 15 04	134	46	0·982	0·983	12 34 48	162	53	118
Morecambe	10 03 38	117	36	309	11 17 23	137	45	0·902	0·883	12 34 52	164	50	121
Newbury	10 02 11	116	38	316	11 18 08	138	48	0·972	0·972	12 38 07	167	53	116
Newcastle	10 06 00	119	37	306	11 19 28	140	45	0·875	0·849	12 36 18	167	50	120
Newry, Co. Down	10 00 42	113	34	310	11 13 16	132	43	0·902	0·883	12 29 59	157	49	124
Northampton	10 03 30	118	38	313	11 19 05	139	47	0·949	0·942	12 38 28	168	53	116
Norwich	10 06 16	121	39	311	11 22 16	143	48	0·933	0·923	12 41 36	173	53	115
Nottingham	10 04 01	118	38	311	11 19 03	139	47	0·929	0·917	12 37 46	167	52	118
Okehampton	10 58 46	112	36	318	11 14 06	133	46	0·995	0·996	12 34 04	161	53	118
Omagh	10 00 27	112	33	309	11 12 26	131	42	0·892	0·869	12 28 35	156	49	125
Oxford	10 02 38	117	38	315	11 18 24	138	47	0·962	0·959	12 38 07	167	53	116
Perth	10 06 09	118	35	303	11 18 00	138	43	0·840	0·804	12 33 12	163	48	124
Portree	10 05 18	116	33	301	11 15 39	135	41	0·817	0·774	12 29 26	159	46	127
St. Helier, Jersey	09 59 14	113	38	322	11 16 02	134	49	0·991	0·993	12 37 28	165	55	114
St. Peter Port, Guernsey	09 59 01	113	38	322	11 15 32	134	48	0·998	0·999	12 36 42	164	55	115
Salisbury	10 01 22	115	38	317	11 17 20	137	47	0·983	0·984	12 37 29	166	54	116
Scarborough	10 06 19	120	38	307	11 20 38	142	46	0·892	0·870	12 38 16	169	51	118
Sheffield	10 04 10	118	37	310	11 18 48	139	46	0·918	0·904	12 37 07	167	51	118
Shrewsbury	10 02 10	116	37	313	11 16 50	136	46	0·939	0·929	12 35 31	164	52	119
Skegness	10 05 49	120	39	310	11 21 10	142	47	0·921	0·907	12 39 55	171	52	116
Sligo	09 59 05	110	33	310	11 10 52	129	42	0·901	0·881	12 27 01	153	49	126
Southampton	10 01 36	116	38	317	11 17 48	137	48	0·987	0·988	12 38 09	167	54	115
Stoke-on-Trent	10 03 04	117	37	312	11 17 45	138	46	0·933	0·918	12 36 17	165	52	119
Stornoway	10 06 24	117	33	299	11 16 04	135	40	0·796	0·748	12 29 00	159	46	128
Stranraer	10 02 45	115	35	307	11 15 16	135	43	0·882	0·857	12 31 37	160	49	123
Stratford-on-Avon	10 02 39	117	38	314	11 18 00	138	47	0·951	0·945	12 37 18	166	52	117
Swindon	10 01 53	116	38	315	11 17 35	137	47	0·969	0·967	12 37 21	166	53	117
Tenby	09 59 06	112	36	316	11 13 41	132	45	0·970	0·968	12 32 47	160	52	120
Tiverton	09 59 27	113	37	318	11 14 54	134	47	0·990	0·992	12 34 51	162	53	118
Tunbridge Wells	10 03 38	118	39	316	11 20 18	140	49	0·977	0·977	12 40 45	170	54	114
Warwick	10 02 52	117	38	313	11 18 12	138	47	0·949	0·942	12 37 26	166	52	117
Weston-super-Mare	10 00 26	114	37	316	11 15 49	135	47	0·977	0·977	12 35 33	163	53	118
Wexford	09 58 15	111	34	315	11 11 51	130	44	0·953	0·947	12 30 02	156	51	122
Weymouth	10 00 11	114	37	318	11 16 10	135	47	0·997	0·999	12 36 33	164	54	116
Workington	10 03 45	117	36	308	11 16 53	137	44	0·887	0·864	12 33 44	163	50	122
Wrexham	10 02 18	116	36	312	11 16 41	136	45	0·930	0·918	12 35 02	164	51	120
Wick	10 09 20	121	35	297	11 19 37	141	42	0·787	0·737	12 32 48	164	46	126
York	10 05 15	119	37	309	11 19 37	140	46	0·902	0·883	12 37 27	168	51	119

Times are given in British Summer Time (BST = GMT + 1ʰ)

Let us suppose that a clock face is superimposed on the Sun's disk with the twelve o'clock position pointing towards the zenith or the point in the sky directly above your head. This point has a position angle of 0°. Moving anticlockwise to the nine o'clock position, the hour hand now points to a position angle of 90°. Continuing the clock face analogy, the hour hand at six o'clock corresponds to 180° and similarly three o'clock corresponds to 270°. Therefore, 313° corresponds to the position of the hour hand at $1^h 34^m$. For a graphical display of position angle, refer to the third or fourth panels of Figure 3.

The next four columns in Table 1 refer to the eclipse circumstances at the moment of maximum eclipse. In Cambridge, this occurs at $11^h 20^m 28^s$ BST when the Sun is at an azimuth of 141°, roughly south east, and an altitude of 48°. The next two columns are the magnitude (Mag) and the obscuration (Obs) of the eclipse. As there is often considerable confusion between these two quantities, an explanation of these terms follows. The magnitude of the eclipse refers to the fraction of the solar diameter covered by the Moon at the moment of greatest eclipse expressed in terms of the solar diameter. This quantity can be greater than one as the apparent diameter of the Moon may be greater than that of the Sun. By definition, the magnitude of an eclipse must be greater than one for a total eclipse to occur. For Cambridge, the magnitude of the eclipse is 0·948. The obscuration, however, is the fraction of the surface of the solar disk covered by the Moon and takes a maximum value of one during totality. It is the obscuration of the Sun which has been plotted in Figure 4. At maximum eclipse, 0·941 or 94·1% of the Sun is obscured by the Moon as seen from Cambridge.

The final four columns refer to fourth contact. Fourth contact or the end of the eclipse for Cambridge occurs at $12^h 40^m 02^s$ BST when the Sun is at an azimuth of 170°, almost due south at an altitude of 53°. The silhouette of the Moon disappears from the Sun's disk at a position angle (PA) of 115°, the position the hour hand of our imaginary clock would occupy at $08^h 10^m$. The partial eclipse as seen from Cambridge is over.

10 — Local circumstances of the total eclipse in the British Isles

The path of totality over the Isles of Scilly, Cornwall, Devon and the Channel Islands is shown in Figure 5. The first to see totality are the Isles of Scilly where Hugh Town on St. Mary's sees $1^m 46^s$ of totality. If you are on the UK mainland south of a line joining Port Isaac in Cornwall and Teignmouth in Devon, you should see a total eclipse. The duration of the eclipse will be very short if you are only just south of this line. For example, Portland Bill lies just outside the path of totality whereas Teignmouth will see only 14^s of totality. Moving south to Falmouth, the duration of totality increases to $2^m 06^s$. In the southern half of the track, St. Anne, on the Channel Island of Alderney, will see $1^m 47^s$ of totality. Guernsey and Jersey are south of the southern limit of totality although Guernsey should see a fine display of Baily's Beads.

Let us suppose we are observing the total eclipse from Falmouth. The information in Table 2 is explained by tracing the course of the eclipse as viewed from Falmouth. The first column of Table 2 is the location. The next four columns refer to first contact and provide the same information as Table 1. Hence, the start of the eclipse or the beginning of the penumbral phase occurs at $09^h 57^m 06^s$ BST. The Sun lies at an azimuth of 111° and an altitude of 36°. The silhouette of the Moon first appears at a position angle (PA) of 320° corresponding to the position of the hour hand at $1^h 20^m$ on the imaginary clock face introduced in Section 9.

Over the next hour and a quarter, more and more of the Sun's disk is covered by the Moon. The sixth column in Table 2 is the time of second contact or the beginning of totality which occurs at $11^h 11^m 15^s$ BST in Falmouth. The next four columns refer to maximum eclipse. The time of maximum eclipse occurs at $11^h 12^m 18^s$ BST when the Sun lies in a south-easterly direction at an azimuth of 130° and an altitude of 46°.

The next column is the duration of totality which is $2^m 06^s$ for Falmouth. This quantity has been calculated on the assumption that the Moon is a smooth sphere. However, the topography of the lunar limb, in particular the presence of deep valleys, can reduce the obscuring effect of the Moon and hence decrease the duration of totality by several seconds. More detailed calculations, taking into account the shape of the Moon's limb, are required for better estimates of the duration of totality for locations close to the limits of the path of totality.

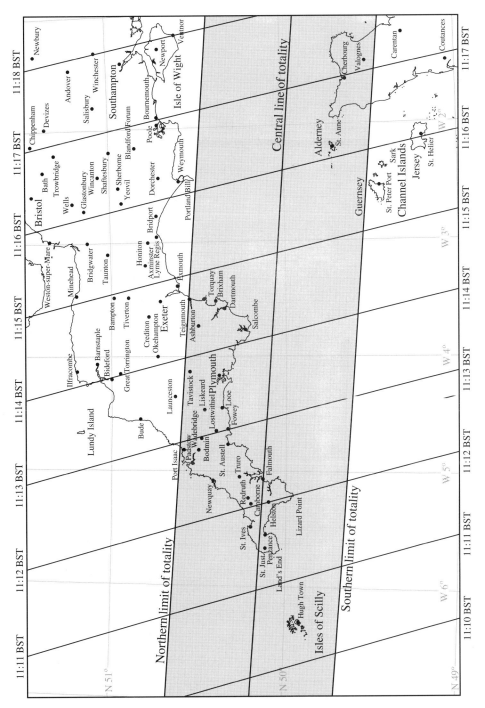

Figure 5: The path of totality over the Isles of Scilly, Cornwall, Devon, the Channel Islands and northern France. The lines crossing the diagram north to south link together locations sharing the same time of maximum eclipse. These lines are drawn at one minute intervals. The times of maximum eclipse, expressed in British Summer Time (BST), are given at the top and bottom of the diagram for each of these lines. The latitude and longitude lines and annotation are shown in grey. The shaded area is the path of totality. A total eclipse should be visible for all locations on the UK mainland south of a line between Port Isaac and Teignmouth. The Isles of Scilly, the Channel Island of Alderney and the northern tip of the Cherbourg peninsula will also experience totality.

Table 2: Local circumstances of the total eclipse in the British Isles

Place	First Contact				Second Contact	Maximum Eclipse				Third Contact	Fourth Contact			
	Time	Az	Alt	PA	Time	Time	Az	Alt	Dur	Time	Time	Az	Alt	PA
	h m s	°	°	°	h m s	h m s	°	°	m s	h m s	h m s	°	°	°
Ashburton	09 58 47	112	37	319	11 13 52	11 14 20	133	47	0 56	11 14 48	12 34 30	161	54	118
Blisland	09 57 53	111	36	319	11 12 30	11 13 03	131	46	1 07	11 13 37	12 33 00	159	53	119
Bodmin	09 57 48	111	36	319	11 12 17	11 12 59	131	46	1 23	11 13 40	12 32 57	159	53	119
Brixham	09 58 55	113	37	319	11 13 49	11 14 37	133	47	1 35	11 15 24	12 34 56	162	54	117
Buckfastleigh	09 58 44	112	37	319	11 13 40	11 14 16	133	47	1 12	11 14 52	12 34 28	161	54	118
Callington	09 58 13	112	36	319	11 12 57	11 13 33	132	46	1 12	11 14 09	12 33 36	160	53	118
Camborne	09 56 58	110	35	320	11 11 00	11 12 02	130	46	2 04	11 13 05	12 32 03	158	53	119
Dartmeet	09 58 42	112	36	319	11 13 53	11 14 11	133	47	0 35	11 14 29	12 34 19	161	54	118
Dartmouth	09 58 47	112	37	319	11 13 36	11 14 28	133	47	1 44	11 15 20	12 34 48	162	54	117
Devonport	09 58 13	112	36	319	11 12 47	11 13 40	132	46	1 46	11 14 33	12 33 51	160	54	118
Falmouth	09 57 06	111	36	320	11 11 15	11 12 18	130	46	2 06	11 13 21	12 32 25	158	54	119
Fowey	09 57 44	111	36	320	11 12 04	11 13 00	131	46	1 53	11 13 57	12 33 06	159	54	119
Gorran Haven	09 57 29	111	36	320	11 11 43	11 12 44	131	46	2 03	11 13 46	12 32 51	159	54	119
Hayle	09 56 48	110	35	320	11 10 47	11 11 50	130	46	2 06	11 12 53	12 31 51	157	53	119
Helston	09 56 52	110	36	320	11 10 57	11 12 00	130	46	2 06	11 13 03	12 32 05	158	54	119
Hugh Town	09 55 41	109	35	321	11 09 34	11 10 28	128	45	1 46	11 11 21	12 30 24	155	53	120
Ivybridge	09 58 28	112	36	319	11 13 11	11 14 00	132	47	1 41	11 14 51	12 34 14	161	54	118
Kingsbridge	09 58 32	112	37	320	11 13 12	11 14 10	133	47	1 56	11 15 08	12 34 30	161	54	117
Kingswear	09 58 48	112	37	319	11 13 38	11 14 30	133	47	1 44	11 15 22	12 34 50	162	54	117
Land's End	09 56 22	110	35	321	11 10 19	11 11 20	129	46	2 03	11 12 21	12 31 21	157	53	120
Liskeard	09 58 02	112	36	319	11 12 36	11 13 19	132	46	1 25	11 14 01	12 33 21	160	53	118
Lizard	09 56 48	110	36	321	11 11 02	11 12 01	130	46	1 59	11 13 00	12 32 13	158	54	119
Looe	09 57 54	111	36	320	11 12 19	11 13 16	131	46	1 52	11 14 12	12 33 24	160	54	118
Lostwithiel	09 57 46	111	36	319	11 12 10	11 13 00	131	46	1 41	11 13 51	12 33 03	159	53	119
Mevagissey	09 57 31	111	36	320	11 11 45	11 12 46	131	46	2 00	11 13 46	12 32 52	159	54	119
Mullion	09 56 49	110	36	321	11 10 58	11 12 00	130	46	2 03	11 13 01	12 32 09	158	54	119
Newquay	09 57 23	111	36	320	11 11 35	11 12 26	131	46	1 42	11 13 17	12 32 22	158	53	119
Newton Abbot	09 58 57	113	37	319	11 14 13	11 14 33	133	47	0 40	11 14 53	12 34 45	162	54	118
Newton Ferrers	09 58 18	112	36	320	11 12 53	11 13 49	132	47	1 53	11 14 46	12 34 04	160	54	118
Padstow	09 57 39	111	36	319	11 12 09	11 12 43	131	46	1 06	11 13 16	12 32 35	159	53	119
Penzance	09 56 37	110	35	320	11 10 35	11 11 37	130	46	2 06	11 12 40	12 31 38	157	53	119
Perrenporth	09 57 14	111	36	320	11 11 21	11 12 18	130	46	1 54	11 13 15	12 32 16	158	53	119
Plymouth	09 58 14	112	36	319	11 12 50	11 13 41	132	46	1 42	11 14 32	12 33 51	160	54	118
Polperro	09 57 51	111	36	320	11 12 14	11 13 10	131	46	1 53	11 14 07	12 33 18	159	54	118
Port Isaac	09 57 49	111	36	319	11 12 35	11 12 54	131	46	0 39	11 13 13	12 32 47	159	53	119
Portreath	09 57 01	110	35	320	11 11 03	11 12 04	130	46	2 02	11 13 05	12 32 04	158	53	119
Prawle Point	09 58 29	112	37	320	11 13 09	11 14 11	133	47	2 04	11 15 13	12 34 35	161	54	117
Redruth	09 57 01	110	36	320	11 11 05	11 12 07	130	46	2 04	11 13 09	12 32 09	158	53	119
Roche	09 57 37	111	36	320	11 11 56	11 12 47	131	46	1 42	11 13 38	12 32 47	159	53	119
St. Agnes	09 57 09	111	36	320	11 11 14	11 12 13	130	46	1 57	11 13 12	12 32 11	158	53	119
St. Anne, Alderney	09 59 37	114	38	321	11 15 15	11 16 08	135	48	1 47	11 17 02	12 37 12	164	55	115
St. Austell	09 57 36	111	36	320	11 11 52	11 12 49	131	46	1 53	11 13 45	12 32 52	159	53	119
St. Columb Major	09 57 32	111	36	319	11 11 50	11 12 39	131	46	1 38	11 13 28	12 32 36	159	53	119
St. Ives	09 56 46	110	35	320	11 10 43	11 11 46	130	46	2 05	11 12 48	12 31 44	157	53	119
St. Just	09 56 30	110	35	320	11 10 24	11 11 27	129	46	2 05	11 12 30	12 31 26	157	53	120
St. Stephen	09 57 29	111	36	320	11 11 44	11 12 40	131	46	1 53	11 13 36	12 32 41	159	53	119
Salcombe	09 58 29	112	37	320	11 13 08	11 14 09	133	47	2 01	11 15 09	12 34 31	161	54	117
Tavistock	09 58 27	112	36	319	11 13 27	11 13 49	132	46	0 44	11 14 11	12 33 53	160	53	118
Teignmouth	09 59 05	113	37	319	11 14 35	11 14 42	133	47	0 14	11 14 49	12 34 54	162	54	117
Torquay	09 58 59	113	37	319	11 14 03	11 14 39	133	47	1 12	11 15 15	12 34 55	162	54	117
Totnes	09 58 45	112	37	319	11 13 37	11 14 22	133	47	1 31	11 15 07	12 34 38	161	54	118
Trenance	09 57 29	111	36	319	11 11 48	11 12 33	131	46	1 30	11 13 18	12 32 27	158	53	119
Truro	09 57 15	111	36	320	11 11 23	11 12 24	130	46	2 01	11 13 24	12 32 26	158	53	119
Wadebridge	09 57 43	111	36	319	11 12 11	11 12 50	131	46	1 19	11 13 29	12 32 46	159	53	119
Yelverton	09 58 26	112	36	319	11 13 15	11 13 51	132	46	1 12	11 14 27	12 33 58	160	54	118

Times are given in British Summer Time (BST = GMT + 1^h)

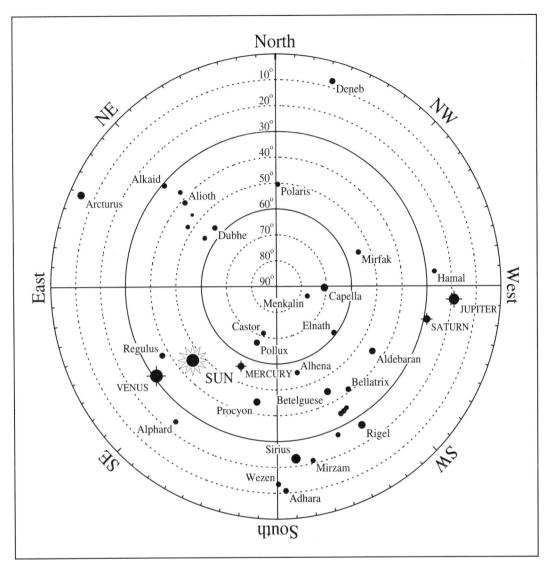

Figure 6: A view of the whole sky as it will appear from Falmouth during totality. The centre of the plot represents the point in the sky directly overhead and altitudes above the horizon are marked in intervals of 10°. Around the edge of the diagram is the horizon where the main compass points are given with tick marks every 5° in azimuth. This diagram is applicable to all those parts of the UK in the path of totality. All the planets visible to the naked eye during totality and the main stars in the constellations of Ursa Major and Orion are plotted in addition to those stars brighter than magnitude 2·0. The size of the symbol is related to the apparent magnitude of the object. The larger the filled circle, the brighter the object.

As the sky darkens just before totality, some of the planets will become visible. Jupiter and Saturn, at magnitudes −2·5 and +0·2 respectively, will be setting in the west and may be difficult to identify. However, Mercury and Venus should be seen quite easily. Mercury is 18° west of the Sun with a magnitude of +0·6 whereas Venus is 15° east of the Sun with a magnitude of −4·1. For many people, this will be their first view of Mercury, a planet which never strays too far from the Sun as seen in our skies. Similarly, some bright stars will also become visible. At the time of the eclipse, the Sun is in the constellation of Cancer, the Crab, a constellation devoid of bright stars. However, bright stars which are relatively close to the eclipsed Sun include *Sirius, Regulus, Castor, Pollux* and *Procyon*.

A simplified sky chart is given in Figure 6. The centre of the plot represents the zenith and altitudes are marked in intervals of 10°. Around the edge of the diagram is the horizon where the main compass points are given with tick marks every 5° in azimuth. Stars brighter than magnitude 2·0 are plotted as well as those planets visible to the naked eye. To identify stars and planets during the total eclipse, hold the map above your head with North pointing in the direction of true north. If you are facing south, the Sun should be on your left hand side in front of you. Although this diagram has been produced for the skies above Falmouth at the time of mid-totality, it should be applicable to all those parts of the UK within the path of totality. The visibility of some or all of these objects will depend on local weather conditions including the presence of haze or mist.

The Perseid meteor shower usually reaches the peak of its activity on August 12th. During totality, the point from which these meteors appear in the sky, known as the radiant, is approximately 50° above the western horizon. Consequently, it is quite possible that meteors may be seen during totality.

Returning to Table 2, the next column is the time of third contact or the end of totality which occurs at 11^h 13^m 21^s BST. The last four columns refer to fourth contact or the end of the penumbral phase of the eclipse. This occurs at 12^h 32^m 25^s BST for Falmouth. The Sun is now at an azimuth of 158°, a south south easterly direction and an altitude of 54°. The silhouette of the Moon leaves the Sun's disk at a position angle of 119° or the position of the hour hand at 08^h 02^m on our imaginary clock face. The eclipse for observers in Falmouth is now complete.

In the Channel Islands, the eclipse is total for those observers on Alderney, the most northerly member of these islands. Table 2 shows that the eclipse begins at 09^h 59^m 37^s BST at St. Anne. The Sun lies at an azimuth of 114° and an altitude of 38°. The silhouette of the Moon appears at a position angle of 321°. Second contact occurs at 11^h 15^m 15^s BST and totality lasts for 1^m 47^s. The duration of totality is somewhat shorter than that for the mainland as Alderney lies further away from the central line of the eclipse. By maximum eclipse at 11^h 16^m 08^s BST, the Sun has reached an azimuth of 135° and an altitude of 48°. Third contact occurs at 11^h 17^m 02^s BST and the eclipse ends at 12^h 37^m 12^s BST when the Sun lies at an azimuth of 164° and an altitude of 55°. The silhouette of the Moon leaves the Sun's disk at a position angle of 115°.

11 — Local circumstances of the eclipse in Europe

Some people may be travelling in Europe at the time of the eclipse. In order to help them get the most out of the event as well, local circumstances have been provided for a range of locations across Europe. The path of totality over Europe is given in Figure 7. The number of locations given on this map is far from exhaustive and must be regarded as a sample only.

Table 3 gives the local circumstances for 55 locations across Europe which experience a partial eclipse. The information is presented in the same format as Table 1 for the UK (see Section 9 for a detailed description). Several large cities across Europe will see more than 99% of the Sun disappear at maximum eclipse. These include Paris (99.4%), Vienna (99.3%) and Budapest (99.4%). Skies will also darken noticeably in cities such as Ankara, Belgrade, Berne, Bonn, Bratislava, Brussels, Frankfurt, Innsbruck, Istanbul, Ljubljana, Zagreb and Zurich where the obscuration is at least 95%.

Table 4 gives the local circumstances for 25 towns and cities across Europe which experience totality and can be used in a similar manner to Table 2 for the UK (see Section 10 for a detailed description). Two capital cities will see totality, namely Luxembourg and Bucharest. Many large cities in the industrial region of southern Germany including Stuttgart and Munich will see in excess of two minutes of totality. Similarly, Szeged in southern Hungary and Arad and Timisoara in western Romania will also see a similar duration of totality.

It is likely that Summer time (daylight-saving time) will be kept in all the countries for which locations are specified in Tables 3 and 4 and Figure 7. In all cases, Summer time is one hour ahead of Standard time. To correct the times given in Tables 3 and 4 from British Summer Time (BST) to Summer time for a specific country you must add the time zone difference for that country. For example, Table 4 gives the time of first contact as 10^h 41^m 22^s BST in Bucharest. As Standard time in Romania is two hours ahead of GMT, we find that the eclipse will start at 12^h 41^m 22^s Summer time in Bucharest.

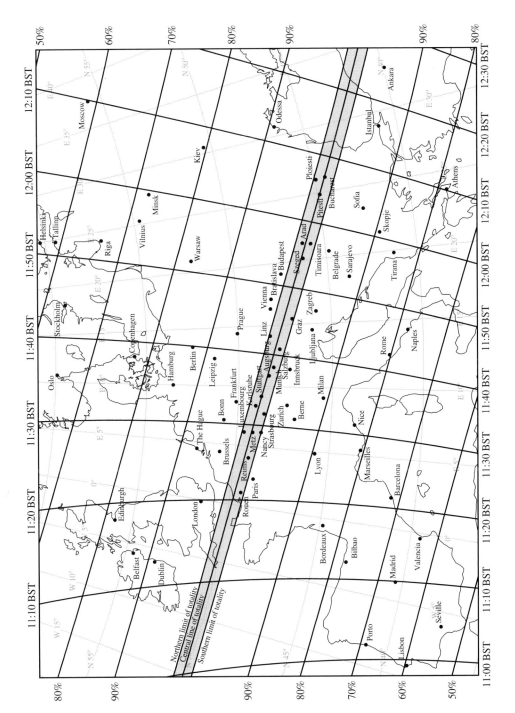

Figure 7: The circumstances of the eclipse for Europe. The near vertical lines link sites having the same times of maximum eclipse whereas those running nearly horizontally link places experiencing the same degree of obscuration at maximum eclipse. Times are given in British Summer Time (BST) in intervals of ten minutes across the top and bottom of the diagram. Tables 3 and 4 are given in terms of BST for consistency with this diagram. The percentage obscuration of the Sun is given on the right and left hand side of the diagram. The latitude and longitude lines and annotation are shown in grey. The shaded area is the path of totality and the northern and southern limits of the path of totality are indicated as well as the central line of the eclipse.

Table 3: Local circumstances of the partial eclipse in Europe

Place	First Contact				Maximum Eclipse					Fourth Contact			
	Time	Az	Alt	PA	Time	Az	Alt	Mag	Obs	Time	Az	Alt	PA
	h m s	°	°	°	h m s	°	°			h m s	°	°	°
Ankara	10 58 10	183	65	291	12 24 55	225	58	0·969	0·967	13 44 59	249	45	061
Athens	10 41 22	151	65	323	12 10 11	204	66	0·822	0·782	13 34 27	239	55	056
Barcelona	10 00 46	111	44	343	11 21 28	135	57	0·772	0·719	12 47 01	175	64	097
Belgrade	10 30 51	147	57	313	11 56 20	186	60	0·978	0·978	13 19 51	222	54	078
Berlin	10 21 10	139	47	303	11 39 51	167	52	0·894	0·872	12 59 13	199	52	103
Berne	10 09 45	124	46	323	11 31 14	152	56	0·956	0·952	12 55 18	189	58	098
Bilbao	09 54 21	107	39	340	11 12 13	127	51	0·816	0·774	12 36 04	159	61	109
Bonn	10 11 29	127	44	313	11 30 28	153	52	0·968	0·967	12 51 47	186	54	105
Bordeaux	09 58 01	111	41	334	11 16 56	133	52	0·868	0·840	12 40 59	167	60	107
Bratislava	10 25 00	142	52	310	11 47 49	176	57	0·988	0·989	13 10 08	211	54	089
Brussels	10 08 06	123	42	314	11 26 15	148	51	0·975	0·975	12 47 22	180	54	109
Budapest	10 28 10	146	54	309	11 51 39	181	58	0·992	0·994	13 13 58	216	53	086
Constanta	10 46 21	168	61	297	12 11 41	209	58	0·998	0·999	13 32 38	237	48	073
Copenhagen	10 22 32	141	44	295	11 38 03	166	49	0·816	0·773	12 54 22	195	49	109
Frankfurt	10 13 10	129	46	313	11 33 00	156	53	0·979	0·980	12 54 48	190	55	102
Gdansk	10 29 44	150	48	292	11 46 48	179	51	0·818	0·777	13 03 25	207	48	103
Hamburg	10 17 26	134	44	303	11 34 42	161	51	0·881	0·856	12 53 23	191	51	108
Helsinki	10 41 32	165	44	273	11 51 23	189	45	0·652	0·570	13 00 15	211	42	112
Innsbruck	10 15 45	131	49	319	11 38 12	161	57	0·984	0·986	13 01 58	199	57	093
Ismir	10 48 01	163	66	312	12 16 35	214	63	0·869	0·842	13 39 30	244	51	057
Istanbul	10 49 13	169	64	302	12 16 26	214	60	0·955	0·950	13 38 09	242	49	064
Kiev	10 47 32	173	55	282	12 07 07	206	53	0·833	0·795	13 23 17	231	45	088
Leipzig	10 18 59	136	47	307	11 38 36	165	53	0·930	0·918	12 59 09	197	53	101
Lisbon	09 45 59	097	34	354	10 59 17	112	47	0·673	0·596	12 20 14	137	61	118
Ljubljana	10 20 26	135	52	319	11 44 22	169	59	0·968	0·967	13 08 32	208	57	086
Lvov	10 36 34	158	54	295	11 57 54	192	55	0·897	0·877	13 17 03	222	49	089
Lyon	10 05 36	119	45	329	11 26 41	145	55	0·911	0·895	12 51 16	183	60	099
Madrid	09 52 41	104	39	348	11 09 53	122	52	0·728	0·664	12 33 38	155	63	109
Marseilles	10 05 42	117	46	336	11 27 48	144	58	0·842	0·807	12 53 28	185	62	094
Milan	10 11 52	125	48	326	11 34 42	155	58	0·922	0·909	12 59 38	195	59	092
Minsk	10 42 46	168	51	281	11 59 25	197	50	0·775	0·722	13 13 52	223	45	098
Moscow	10 58 06	189	49	263	12 09 49	214	46	0·665	0·587	13 18 28	234	39	100
Naples	10 20 46	130	55	334	11 47 03	168	64	0·820	0·780	13 13 21	214	61	073
Nice	10 08 33	121	48	333	11 31 21	149	58	0·862	0·833	12 57 02	190	61	091
Odessa	10 49 07	174	59	288	12 12 14	211	56	0·924	0·911	13 30 54	237	46	078
Oslo	10 24 36	141	41	286	11 35 27	164	45	0·718	0·651	12 47 11	189	45	118
Paris	10 04 06	119	42	321	11 22 47	142	51	0·992	0·994	12 45 11	175	56	108
Porto	09 47 08	099	34	346	11 01 37	115	47	0·748	0·689	12 23 24	142	59	118
Prague	10 21 23	139	49	308	11 42 22	169	55	0·953	0·948	13 03 43	203	53	096
Riga	10 38 41	162	47	280	11 52 29	189	48	0·727	0·663	13 05 04	214	45	106
Rome	10 17 13	127	53	333	11 42 36	163	63	0·838	0·803	13 08 49	207	61	078
Sarajevo	10 27 19	141	56	319	11 53 13	181	61	0·936	0·926	13 17 45	219	56	077
Seville	09 49 46	099	37	358	11 04 21	115	51	0·632	0·547	12 26 16	144	64	112
Skopje	10 33 40	147	60	319	12 00 52	191	63	0·909	0·892	13 25 16	228	55	069
Sofia	10 36 55	153	60	313	12 03 47	196	62	0·944	0·937	13 27 19	231	53	070
Stockholm	10 32 23	153	44	282	11 43 56	177	46	0·703	0·633	12 55 22	201	45	113
Tallinn	10 40 50	164	45	274	11 51 37	189	46	0·669	0·591	13 01 23	212	43	111
The Hague	10 09 09	124	42	311	11 26 24	149	50	0·940	0·931	12 46 27	179	53	111
Tirana	10 30 56	143	59	324	11 58 18	187	64	0·878	0·852	13 23 21	226	57	068
Valencia	09 57 07	106	42	350	11 16 07	127	56	0·706	0·637	12 40 57	165	65	101
Vienna	10 23 45	141	52	311	11 46 25	174	57	0·991	0·993	13 08 52	209	54	090
Vilnius	10 39 33	163	50	283	11 55 44	192	50	0·772	0·718	13 10 13	218	46	100
Warsaw	10 32 14	153	51	294	11 51 25	184	53	0·857	0·826	13 09 29	214	49	097
Zagreb	10 22 50	138	53	318	11 47 11	173	59	0·971	0·970	13 11 16	211	56	084
Zurich	10 11 31	126	47	321	11 33 07	155	56	0·973	0·973	12 56 55	192	57	097

Times are given in British Summer Time (BST = GMT + 1[h])

Table 4: Local circumstances of the total eclipse in Europe

Place	First Contact Time	Az	Alt	PA	Second Contact Time	Maximum Eclipse Time	Az	Alt	Dur	Third Contact Time	Fourth Contact Time	Az	Alt	PA
	h m s	°	°	°	h m s	h m s	°	°	m s	h m s	h m s	°	°	°
Amiens	10 04 52	120	41	318	11 22 00	11 22 57	143	51	1 55	11 23 55	12 44 37	175	55	110
Arad	10 32 06	150	56	308	11 55 30	11 56 40	188	59	2 19	11 57 49	13 19 11	222	53	081
Augsburg	10 15 23	131	48	316	11 35 48	11 36 59	161	56	2 21	11 38 09	13 00 01	197	56	096
Bucharest	10 41 22	161	60	302	12 05 43	12 06 56	202	59	2 27	12 08 09	13 28 41	233	50	074
Cherbourg	10 00 10	114	38	321	11 16 09	11 16 58	136	49	1 38	11 17 47	12 38 12	166	55	114
Dieppe	10 03 27	118	40	319	11 20 03	11 21 06	141	50	2 06	11 22 09	12 42 36	172	55	111
Graz	10 22 06	138	52	315	11 44 49	11 45 30	172	58	1 22	11 46 11	13 08 53	209	55	088
Karlsruhe	10 12 10	128	46	317	11 31 34	11 32 40	155	54	2 12	11 33 46	12 55 19	190	56	100
Le Havre	10 02 00	116	40	320	11 18 43	11 19 32	139	50	1 38	11 20 21	12 41 11	170	55	112
Linz	10 20 33	137	50	313	11 42 32	11 42 53	169	57	0 43	11 43 14	13 05 36	205	55	092
Luxembourg	10 09 28	125	44	317	11 28 16	11 28 58	151	53	1 26	11 29 41	12 51 10	185	56	104
Metz	10 09 11	124	44	318	11 27 51	11 28 59	150	53	2 18	11 30 08	12 51 32	185	56	103
Munich	10 16 18	132	49	316	11 37 07	11 38 14	162	56	2 12	11 39 20	13 01 23	199	56	095
Pitesti	10 38 52	158	59	304	12 03 02	12 04 15	198	59	2 27	12 05 29	13 26 17	230	51	076
Ploiesti	10 41 01	161	59	302	12 05 28	12 06 15	201	59	1 32	12 07 01	13 27 47	232	50	075
Reims	10 06 30	121	43	319	11 24 31	11 25 33	146	52	2 05	11 26 35	12 47 53	179	56	106
Rimnicu-Vilcea	10 37 51	157	58	305	12 01 54	12 03 07	197	59	2 27	12 04 20	13 25 13	229	51	076
Rouen	10 03 03	117	40	320	11 20 07	11 20 58	140	50	1 42	11 21 49	12 42 49	172	56	110
Saarbrucken	10 10 20	126	45	317	11 29 13	11 30 20	152	53	2 13	11 31 26	12 52 49	187	56	103
Salzburg	10 18 25	134	50	316	11 39 50	11 40 54	166	57	2 07	11 41 57	13 04 08	202	56	092
Strasbourg	10 11 00	126	46	318	11 30 52	11 31 38	154	54	1 32	11 32 24	12 54 37	189	56	100
Stuttgart	10 13 06	129	47	317	11 32 50	11 34 01	157	55	2 21	11 35 12	12 56 51	192	56	099
Szeged	10 30 01	147	55	310	11 53 17	11 54 30	185	59	2 25	11 55 42	13 17 19	220	54	082
Timisoara	10 31 58	149	56	309	11 55 46	11 56 50	188	59	2 08	11 57 54	13 19 39	222	53	080
Varna	10 45 30	166	61	300	12 11 36	12 11 38	208	59	0 04	12 11 40	13 33 08	238	49	070

Times are given in British Summer Time (BST = GMT + 1ʰ)

12 — Observing the eclipse

There are many ways to observe a total eclipse of the Sun. The primary consideration should always be safety. Jeopardizing your eyesight to watch the eclipse using inadequate precautions can never be justified by the rarity of such an event over the UK. **The only time it is safe to look directly at the Sun is during totality. At any other time, the ultraviolet and infrared radiation will damage your eyesight even though you may not feel any discomfort. Do not stare at the Sun.** Be aware that the transition from totality to the partial phase of the eclipse occurs very rapidly. Observing the Sun with any form of optical aid is potentially **very** dangerous unless you know what you are doing. If you are not sure about what you are attempting to do, the best advice is not to do it at all!

There are several methods of observing the partial phases of the eclipse safely. The simplest method is pinhole projection which requires two pieces of stiff cardboard. A clean pinhole is punched in one piece of card. Standing with your back to the Sun, arrange the pieces of card so that sunlight passes through the hole in the first piece of card and is projected on to the second piece of card held about a metre from the first. An inverted image of the Sun will be seen approximately one centimetre in diameter. Make sure the pinhole is not too wide otherwise no image will be formed. The size of the image can be adjusted by changing the separation between the two pieces of card. Do **not** look through the pinhole at the Sun.

Projecting the Sun using binoculars can also give several people the opportunity to observe the eclipse simultaneously. Keeping the objective cover on one side of the binoculars, a sheet of cardboard is placed around the other objective lens of the binoculars. This acts as a shade for a second sheet of cardboard placed approximately 30 centimetres behind the eyepieces of the binoculars upon which the image of the Sun can be projected. Aligning the binoculars should be done by minimizing the shadow of the binoculars and **not** by looking through them. The image should be focused using the focusing knob and adjusting the distance between the binoculars and the projection screen. A similar method can be adopted for use with a small refracting telescope. Do **not** use the finder telescope to align the main telescope.

Solar viewers made of aluminised mylar may be used safely. However, they **must** be checked for flaws which might allow direct sunlight to reach your eyes. The best type of filter to use is one employing two layers of aluminised mylar film. This minimizes the possibility of an alignment of pinhole flaws in the aluminium coatings. The viewer supplied with this guide uses this form of construction. Welder's goggles are also suitable for observing the eclipse as long as they have a rating of 14 or higher and have been checked for their infrared transmission characteristics (see Amendment 3 to BS679:1959; "Filters for use during welding and similar industrial operations"). More specialised camera and telescope filters are also available which are generally expensive and only available from specialist suppliers (see Section 17).

Sunglasses of any type **must not** be used for looking at the Sun. They do not block those wavelengths of light likely to damage your eyes nor do they provide the necessary reduction in the intensity of incoming light. The damaging radiation from the Sun is also unaffected by polaroid sunglasses. Smoked glass can provide some protection if the glass is large enough and the density of the carbon deposit is sufficiently high. Unfortunately, making a uniformly dark filter is difficult and the degree of protection cannot be guaranteed. As a result, this method is **not** recommended. Fully-exposed and developed film should **not** be used. Colour film and chromogenic black and white films are totally unsuitable as harmful infrared radiation is not blocked by the coloured dyes used in these preparations. Under **no** circumstances should gelatin neutral density filters be used. Standard 35 millimetre negatives of any type are physically too small to be used as solar filters. However, certain types of fully exposed and developed black and white film using metallic silver can be used as solar filters. Two layers of film must be used for brief views of the Sun amounting to less than about 30 seconds in duration. If you are unsure about the type of film you have do **not** use it!

13 — Recording the eclipse

For people who wish to retain some record of the eclipse, videography and photography are possible. Like the eye, the detector in the average video camera will be destroyed by exposing it directly to full sunlight. In general, exposure times and aperture settings are dealt with automatically by the electronic metering system within the video camera. However, some form of aluminised mylar or glass solar filter capable of cutting the amount of light and heat down by a factor of approximately 100 000, corresponding to a neutral density of 5·0, is required during the partial phases of the eclipse to allow suitable exposures times and aperture stops to be set by the metering system in the camera. During totality, the filter should be removed. Caution **must** also be exercised when aligning the video camera with the Sun.

Many people will try to photograph the eclipse. A normal camera lens with a 50 millimetre focal length will produce an image of the Sun some 0·5 millimetres in diameter. Consequently, a telephoto lens is necessary to give an acceptable image size. A 500 millimetre lens would produce an image of nearly 5 millimetres across. To capture the Sun's corona on film, a lens of approximately 1000 millimetres represents the best compromise between the necessary field of view and an acceptable image size. Photography during partial phases will require some form of filtering. As in the case of videography, a filter which cuts the amount of light and heat down by a factor of 100 000 or so is recommended. Care **must** be exercised when setting up the camera because using the optics in the camera viewfinder, as you would for normal photography, will damage your eyesight. A similar warning applies to the use of a single lens reflex (SLR) camera as you are using the camera lens to view the scene you are about to photograph. Exposure times will depend on the amount of filtering. Since there is plenty of light, a film speed of ASA 50 to 100 is suitable. Experimenting on an uneclipsed Sun is a good way to gauge exposure times and using a filter of neutral density 5·0 with ASA 100 film at f/8 would probably require an exposure of 1/125 of a second.

Photography during totality does not require a filter. Assuming you are using ASA 100 film at f/8, prominences could be photographed with an exposure of about 1/60 second. To capture the corona would require an exposure of between 1/8 second and 1/2 second. The key to successful photography is to bracket your exposure by several f-stops. No single exposure time is the correct one. The Sun is not the only object you might photograph during the eclipse. Many photographers try to capture the effect the eclipse has on their surroundings.

Here are two pieces of advice from veteran eclipse watchers. If this is your first total eclipse, it is better to watch it rather than to try and photograph it. Professional photographs will be available after the eclipse of a quality exceeding anything most amateurs might achieve. Secondly, for those people who own a camera with a built-in automatic flash gun, don't use it! You will only cause consternation amongst your fellow eclipse watchers when their dark adaption is ruined by the discharge of a flash gun triggered by the low light levels during totality. However, if you are seriously considering photographing the eclipse, try consulting the books listed in Section 18.

It has been calculated that on average a total eclipse will be visible at a given location on the Earth every 400 years or so. It is therefore an opportunity not to be missed. Give yourself time to stand and take in the awesome spectacle. If this is your first total eclipse then watch the eclipse rather than succumb to the temptation of trying to take photographs of it. Wherever you go to watch the eclipse, enjoy this once in a lifetime event but above all else take care.

14 — Weather along the path of totality

The following information is by no means a definitive description of weather conditions over the path of totality in the UK, it is simply a guide to likely weather patterns. To see the eclipse properly good weather conditions, particularly minimal cloud cover, are vital. Unfortunately, even in August, the weather in the UK cannot be predicted with any great accuracy. In Europe, there is a somewhat better chance of seeing the eclipse the further east you travel. To be sure of seeing this eclipse, a visit to the desert regions of Turkey, Iran or Iraq is recommended.

The average rainfall in south-west England during August is approximately 100 millimetres. This decreases to around 75 millimetres in the Isles of Scilly and around 60 millimetres in the Channel Islands. If rainfall does occur it is likely to be of a showery nature. On average, thunderstorms are likely to occur on two days of the month in the Channel Islands, on one day of the month in Cornwall and on only half a day in the Isles of Scilly. May is the sunniest month in the Isles of Scilly whereas June is the sunniest month in the Channel Islands and Cornwall. The Channel Islands have the highest average total number of hours of sunshine in August at around 220 hours. Similarly, the Isles of Scilly have about 205 hours and Devon and Cornwall have about 180 hours. Examining the figures more closely, the Channel Islands have more than 9 hours of sunshine per day for nearly half of August and two thirds of August have more than six hours of sunshine. In Cornwall, only one quarter of the month has more than 9 hours of sunshine a day and half the month has more than 6 hours of sunshine per day.

Much of the sunshine in coastal areas of the south-west of England and the Channel Islands occurs in the afternoon period for different reasons. The opposite is true for inland regions of Cornwall and Devon. Weather records show that during the morning coastal regions of south-west England are affected by cloud around dawn which gradually disperses throughout the day. Much of this area spends 50% of its daylight hours under skies with more than 75% cloud cover. Observers in Cornwall and the Isles of Scilly may have their view of the eclipse disrupted by clouds because as much as two thirds of the sky may be affected by cloud at the time of the eclipse. However, the Channel Islands do appear to fare a little better. Records show that the problem here may be early morning fog. Approximately one quarter of the month is affected by such fog. Once this early morning fog has dispersed, the skies are somewhat clearer than the mainland.

On balance, there is probably little to choose between the weather in south-west England and the Channel Islands. Local weather conditions may vary greatly between locations separated by as little as 30 kilometres. As far as Cornwall is concerned, the prospects of seeing the eclipse may improve marginally the further south west you go. In the Channel Islands, Alderney being a relatively small, flat island may fare quite well. Anecdotal evidence indicates that Alderney has been clear every 11th August for the past several years!

15 — Future eclipses of the Sun in the British Isles

Although the Channel Islands will see another total eclipse of the Sun lasting a little over two and a half minutes early on the morning of 3rd September 2081, the eclipse of 11th August 1999 will be the last opportunity to see a total eclipse of the Sun in the UK mainland for another 90 years. On 23rd September 2090, the south-western tip of the Irish Republic, south-west England, most of the south coast of England and the Channel Islands will again see a total eclipse of the Sun lasting a little over two and a half minutes just before sunset. As the path of totality is more than 440 kilometres wide, totality will be seen by much of northern France as well. Most of the UK will also witness a partially-eclipsed Sun at sunset.

The next two total eclipses will occur in quick succession. The first occurs on the morning of the 3rd June 2133 over the Outer Hebrides, the Shetland Islands and the north-west tip of Scotland. Stornoway will see approximately two and a half minutes of totality being on the southern side of an eclipse path some 280 kilometres wide. The second eclipse occurs shortly after sunrise on 7th October 2135 over central and southern Scotland and north-east England. The path of totality is approximately 180 kilometres wide and the duration of totality in Glasgow is a little over two and a half minutes.

Seven years later, the Channel Islands will see yet another total eclipse of the Sun early on the morning of 25th May 2142. St. Helier, on Jersey, is on the northern side of the 180 kilometre-wide eclipse path and will see approximately three minutes of totality. After a further nine years, another total eclipse will occur in the early evening of 14th June 2151. It will be seen as total from Northern Ireland, north Wales, south-west Scotland, northern England, the Midlands and East Anglia. The path of totality is some 240 kilometres wide resulting in Leeds seeing two and half minutes of totality.

On a shorter timescale, there are three solar eclipses worthy of some discussion in the next 30 years or so. The solar eclipse of 31st May 2003 is an annular eclipse. Parts of northern Scotland will see it as an annular eclipse but for most observers on the UK mainland the eclipse will be seen as a partial one during sunrise. The skies over the UK and the Irish Republic will darken quite substantially on the morning of 20th March 2015. The track of this total eclipse passes over the northern Atlantic Ocean between Iceland and northern Scotland reaching as far as the North Pole. The obscuration of the Sun will be about 85% as seen from south-east England rising to around 90% for north-west Scotland. Another total eclipse track passing to the west of the Irish Republic is that of 12th August 2026 which will again bring a substantial darkening of the sky just before sunset. Details of these and other eclipses will be available in future publications of HM Nautical Almanac Office.

16 — A quick summary

If you want to use this guide as a quick reference to determine what you are likely to see at a specific location in the UK, the Irish Republic or the Channel Islands, please follow these steps (Tables and figures in parentheses refer to those observers situated in Europe):

- Identify your location on Figure 4 (Figure 7). By comparing your geographical position with the nearly horizontal lines on the map, you can determine how much of the Sun will be obscured. You will also be able to estimate the time of maximum eclipse from the near vertical lines.

- If you think the location from which you will observe the eclipse lies close to path of totality, confirmation can be obtained using Figure 5 (Figure 7). If you are in the shaded area of the map, you should see a total eclipse of the Sun.

- If you are likely to see a partial eclipse, look in Table 1 (Table 3) for a city or town close to your location. Reading across the table will give you the times and positions of the Sun at the start of the eclipse, maximum eclipse and the end of the eclipse along with the relevant obscuration. The position angle of the appearance and disappearance of the silhouette of the Moon on the Sun's disk is also given.

- If you are likely to see a total eclipse, look in Table 2 (Table 4) for a town or village close to your location. Reading across the table will give you the times and positions of the Sun at the start of the eclipse, the beginning and end of totality and the end of the eclipse. The position angle of the appearance and disappearance of the silhouette of the Moon on the

Sun's disk is also given. Figure 6 will give you some idea of what objects will be visible in the sky during totality.

- If you want to see how the eclipse progresses and to visualize the position angle information provided in Tables 1 and 2 (Tables 3 and 4), refer to Figure 3. This diagram may also prove helpful in predicting the appearance of Baily's Beads. They may be visible where there is a sizeable gap between the solid outline of the Moon and the photospheric disk of the Sun.

To observe the eclipse safely, **do not** use the following methods to watch the partial phases of the eclipse as eye damage may result:

- Sunglasses of any type
- Gelatin filters
- Fully exposed and developed colour film
- Fully exposed and developed black and white negatives in general
- Smoked glass

The following methods can be used to observe the partial phase but remember to exercise caution in their use:

- Pinhole projection
- Projection using binoculars or a small telescope
- Welder's goggles rated at 14 or higher
- Aluminised mylar filters

Following these simple rules should minimize the possibility of damaging your eyesight. Even if you are using the correct eye protection, do **not** stare at the Sun for long periods.

17 — The aluminised mylar eclipse viewer

Inside the back cover of this guide, an eclipse viewer has been provided to allow observation of the partial phase of the eclipse. The viewer is constructed from a sandwich of two layers of aluminised mylar cemented together with the aluminium coating on the inside. This reduces the intensity of sunlight to a safe level. Extra eclipse viewers and other solar filters can be obtained from Eclipse99 Limited, Belle Etoile, Rue du Hamel, Castel, Guernsey GY5 7QJ. Extra eclipse viewers can also be purchased from the Royal Greenwich Observatory.

Certification under the provisions of the *Personal Protective Equipment (EC Directive) Regulations 1992* for the UK and Council Directive 89/686/EEC for the European Union has been given to the eclipse viewers provided with this guide. Only viewers carrying the CE mark have been tested successfully under these regulations. Under **no** circumstances should these viewers be used with any other optical devices. People suffering from eye disease or who have had recent eye surgery should seek medical advice before using these viewers. It is also important to remember that the mylar can be damaged by puncturing with a sharp object or by heat sufficient to melt the mylar. **Check the viewer thoroughly for damage before use**.

18 — Useful references

- *The Cambridge Eclipse Photography Guide* by Jay M. Pasachoff and Michael Covington and published by Cambridge University Press.

- *Totality: Eclipses of the Sun* by Mark Littman and Ken Willcox and published by the University of Hawaii Press.

- *Total Eclipses of the Sun* by Jack B. Zirker and published by Van Nostrand Reinhold Limited.

- *UK Solar Eclipses from Year 1 (an anthology of 3,000 years of solar eclipses)* by Sheridan Williams and published by Clock Tower Press.

- HM Nautical Almanac Office provides information on a wide variety of topics associated with the eclipse on our Web site at http://www.ast.cam.ac.uk/eclipse99/.

Printed in the United Kingdom for the Royal Greenwich Observatory by The Papworth Press

PUBLICATIONS OF HM NAUTICAL ALMANAC OFFICE

The Astronomical Almanac contains ephemerides of the Sun, Moon, planets and their natural satellites, as well as data on eclipses and other astronomical phenomena.

Astronomical Phenomena contains data on the principal astronomical phenomena of the Sun, Moon and planets (including eclipses), the times of rising and setting of the Sun and Moon at latitudes between S 55° and N 66°, and calendarial data.

The Nautical Almanac contains ephemerides at an interval of one hour and auxiliary astronomical data for marine navigation.

Sight Reduction Tables for Air Navigation (AP3270), 3 volumes. Volume 1, selected stars for epoch 2000·0, containing the altitude to 1' and true azimuth to 1° for the seven stars most suitable for navigation, for the complete range of latitudes and hour angles of Aries. Volumes 2 and 3 contain values of the altitude to 1' and azimuth to 1° for integral degrees of declination from N 29° to S 29°, for the complete range of latitudes and for all hour angles at which the zenith distance is less than 95° providing for sights of the Sun, Moon and planets.

Planetary and Lunar Coordinates, 1984–2000 provides low-precision astronomical data for use in advance of the annual ephemerides and for other purposes. It contains heliocentric, geocentric, spherical and rectangular coordinates of the Sun, Moon and planets, eclipse data, and auxiliary data, such as orbital elements and precessional constants.

All the above publications are prepared jointly by HM Nautical Almanac Office, Royal Greenwich Observatory, and the Nautical Almanac Office of the United States Naval Observatory, and are published jointly by The Stationery Office (TSO) and the United States Government Printing Office.

The UK Air Almanac contains information necessary for the planning of aircraft movements including rising and setting times for the Sun and Moon, twilight times and percentage illumination of the Moon.

Sight Reduction Tables for Marine Navigation (NP 401), 6 volumes. This series is designed to effect all solutions of the navigational triangle, given two sides and the included angle to find the third side and an adjacent angle; the tables are arranged to facilitate rapid position finding and are intended for use with *The Nautical Almanac*. Explanatory material and auxiliary tables are included in all volumes.

The Star Almanac for Land Surveyors contains the Greenwich hour angle of Aries and the position of the Sun, tabulated for every six hours, and represented by monthly polynomial coefficients. Positions of all stars brighter than magnitude 4·0 are tabulated monthly to a precision of 0^s1 in right ascension and 1″ in declination. Coefficients for calculating the Greenwich Hour angle and declination (Dec) of all the stars published in *The Star Almanac for Land Surveyors*, accurate to about 1″, for 1998 are available on floppy disk. The polynomial coefficients for calculating R, Dec, E and semi-diameter of the Sun are also included. This publication is available from TSO and from UNIPUB, 4611/F Assembly Drive, Lanham, MD 20706-4391, USA.

Compact Data for Navigation and Astronomy for 1996–2000 contains data, which are mainly in the form of polynomial coefficients, for use by navigators and astronomers to calculate the positions of the Sun, Moon, navigational planets and bright stars using a small programmable calculator or personal computer. A 3.5-inch disk for IBM PC and compatibles is included. It contains the astronomical tabular data in ASCII files and NAVPAC, an interactive software package based on the methods in the book. This publication is available from TSO and from UNIPUB, 4611/F Assembly Drive, Lanham, MD 20706-4391, USA.

Further details about the publications and services provided by HM Nautical Almanac Office may be found on our Web site at http://www.ast.cam.ac.uk/nao/.